C000224812

This book comes
with lots of love from

....

LOVE

EGMONT

LOVE

Written by Helen Ford
Illustrated by Simon Taylor-Kielty

EGMONT

We bring stories to life

First published in Great Britain 2011
by Egmont UK Limited
239 Kensington High Street, London W8 6SA

Text copyright © 2011 Egmont UK Limited
Illustrations copyright © 2011 Hallmark Cards plc

ISBN 978 1 4052 5720 6
1 3 5 7 9 10 8 6 4 2

Printed in Singapore

All rights reserved

What's Love?
Now that's a tough one,
Wherever do I start?
I guess the thing that I should do
Is say what's in my heart.

Love is doing nothing much
Just snuggled up in bed.
Thinking there's no place at all
I'd rather be instead.

Love is twirling hand in hand,
Slow dancing to a song.

Love is realising
You've been talking all night long.

Love is that connection
Even when you are apart.
With love you can be miles away
But still in someone's heart.

Love is that special moment
When you both just kind of know,
You've found 'The One', your soulmate,
And you'll never let them go.

Love is lots of laughter
And some dinner on a tray.
Hoping that the moment lasts
Forever and a day.

Love is watching movies
In your pyjamas, but not caring.
Love is having chocolate
That, for once, you don't mind sharing.

Love is feeling happy
Even first thing in the morning.
Love is cuddles and a kiss
Without a moment's warning.

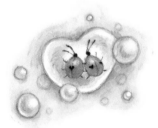

Love is acting like big kids
When no one else is looking.

Love is, 'Put your feet up, Dear,
And let me do the cooking.'

Love is waking up each day
Just knowing that it's true,
Someone thinks you're gorgeous,
Just because you're YOU!

Love is lazy weekends,
Cups of tea and toast.
Reading through the papers
Then a massive Sunday roast.

Love is having holidays
And saying, 'This is bliss.
If we won the lottery
We'd always live like this!'

Love is coming home
When you've had a busy day.
And getting such a lovely hug
Your troubles melt away.

Love is always making time
When you're feeling blue.
A nice romantic meal,
With a glass of wine or two.

Love is years together
And not one bit has been boring.
Love is ice cold feet in bed
And putting up with snoring.

Love is reminiscing all
About when you first met.
So many magic moments
You know you won't forget.

Love is also knowing
That although those days were fun,
There'll always be tomorrow
And the best is yet to come.

Love is knowing deep inside
That this will never end.
Because the person that you love
Is also your best friend.

What's Love?
Not such a tough one,
No need to think it through.
I know exactly what Love is,
Love is me and you.